CW00540530

Emma Farrarons

graphic designer. Born on the island of Cebu in the
Philippines, Emma grew up in Paris. She illustrates
and designs books, posters and stationery.

She was trained in illustration at the Edinburgh
College of Art and l'École nationale supérieure des Arts,
Décoratifs. She completed a textile and printmaking course
at Capellagården school in Sweden and has a particular
love of pattern and fabric print. She is inspired by French,
Scandinavian and Japanese design.

When she is not drawing and designing, Emma
enjoys cookery, sewing, travel and practising mindfulness.
She lives in London with her husband and son.

Share your creations using
#mindfulnesscolouringbook
Visit the Mindfulness Colouring website at
www.mindfulnesscolouring.com
See more of Emma's work on social media
@emmafarrarons

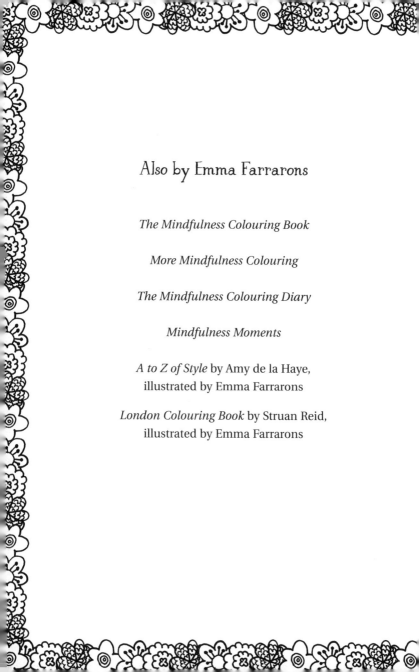

Also by Emma Farrarons

The Mindfulness Colouring Book

More Mindfulness Colouring

The Mindfulness Colouring Diary

Mindfulness Moments

A to Z of Style by Amy de la Haye,
illustrated by Emma Farrarons

London Colouring Book by Struan Reid,
illustrated by Emma Farrarons

Emma Farrarons

ART OF MINDFULNESS

Anti-stress drawing,
colouring and hand lettering

First published 2018 by Boxtree
an imprint of Pan Macmillan
20 New Wharf Road, London N1 9RR
Associated companies throughout the world
www.panmacmillan.com

ISBN 978-0-7522-6594-0

Copyright © Emma Farrarons 2018

The right of Emma Farrarons to be identified as the
author of this work has been asserted by her in accordance
with the Copyright, Designs and Patents Act 1988.

All rights reserved. No part of this publication may be reproduced,
stored in a retrieval system, or transmitted, in any form, or by any means
(electronic, mechanical, photocopying, recording or otherwise)
without the prior written permission of the publisher.

Pan Macmillan does not have any control over, or any responsibility for,
any author or third-party websites referred to in or on this book.

1 3 5 7 9 8 6 4 2

A CIP catalogue record for this book is available from the British Library.

Printed and bound in Italy

This book is sold subject to the condition that it shall not, by way of
trade or otherwise, be lent, hired out, or otherwise circulated without
the publisher's prior consent in any form of binding or cover other than
that in which it is published and without a similar condition including
this condition being imposed on the subsequent purchaser.

Visit **www.panmacmillan.com** to read more about all our books
and to buy them. You will also find features, author interviews and
news of any author events, and you can sign up for e-newsletters
so that you're always first to hear about our new releases.

For Therese Estacion

INTRODUCTION

Mindfulness meditation is all about paying attention to the present moment. Almost any activity, done right, can be an effective exercise in mindfulness and colouring in, with the gentle action of putting pen to paper, is well designed to help clear your mind of excess thoughts while you focus on the task at hand.

Emma Farrarons's Mindfulness Colouring series has helped a million people worldwide find peace and calm in a busy world, with her beautiful templates of patterns and peaceful scenes to adorn with colour. Now *Art of Mindfulness* goes a few steps further to offer more activities in guided creativity.

You'll find stunning scenes to colour in but also motifs to repeat, drawings to complete and handwritten lettering to practise. Offering much more than a colouring book, we hope you'll enjoy colouring and completing Emma's *Art of Mindfulness* in your own style.

Add more detail to the
fox's tail and colour in.

Fill in the blank circles.

Colour in
this forest fox.

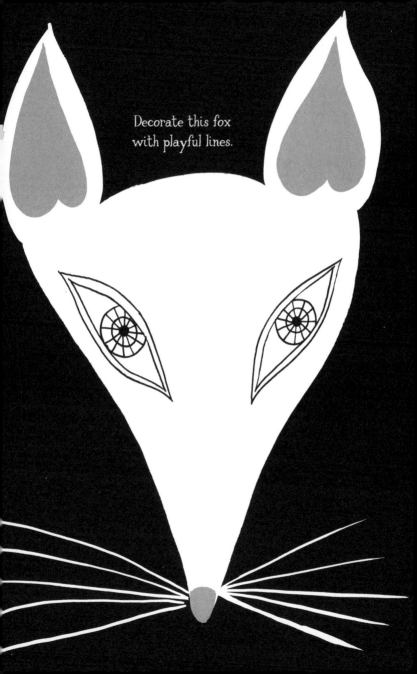

Decorate this fox
with playful lines.

Trace over
these flowers.

Decorate the
roofs with colour -
or patterns!

Fill this
page with
waves.

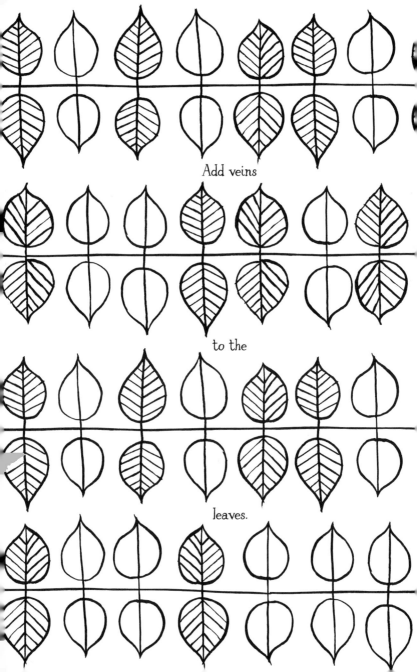

Add veins

to the

leaves.

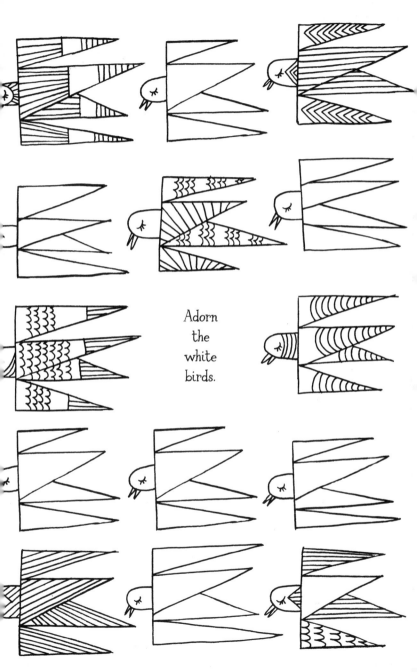

Adorn
the
white
birds.

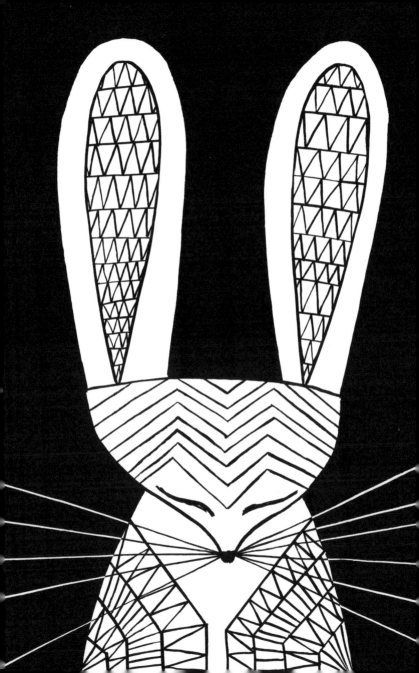

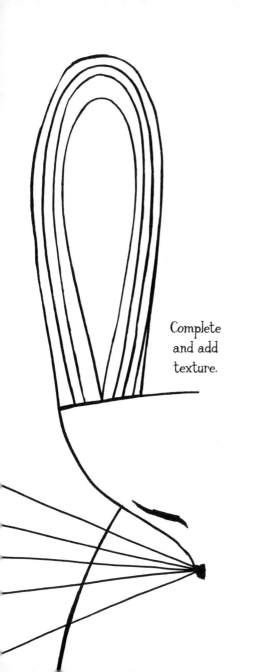

Complete
and add
texture.

Decorate the
dragonflies.

A simple, leafy and mindful hand lettering activity.

a   *a*

b   *b*

c   *c*

d   *d*

e   *e*

f   *f*

g g

h h

i i

j j

k k

l l

m m

n

o

p

q

r

s

t

u u

v v

w w

x x

y y

z z

tree

forest

moon

dream

air

cloud

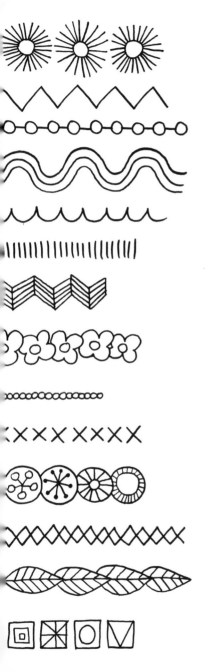

Add patterns
to the owl
and his tree.

Decorate the squirrel, moon and stars.

What colour is this squirrel?

the brighter the stars

Fyodor Dostoevsky

Repeat and complete.

Bring these
birch trees to life.

Add detail to the petals.

Complete the
mountain scenery.

Create and colour your own alphabet.

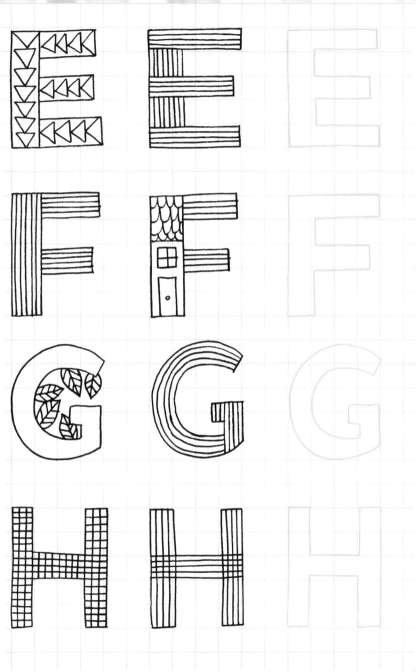

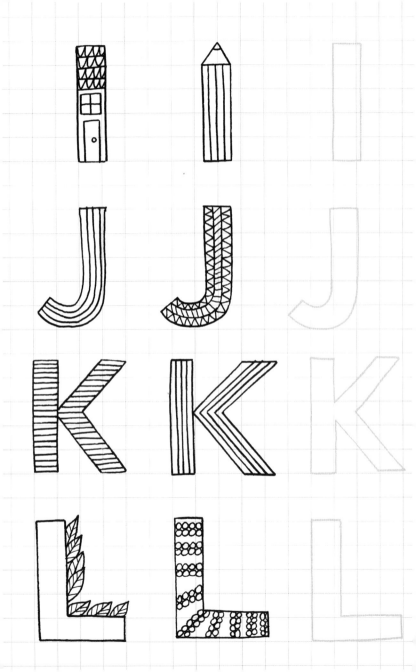

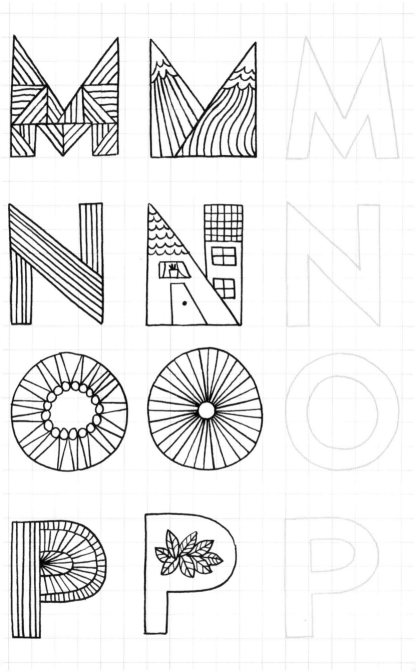

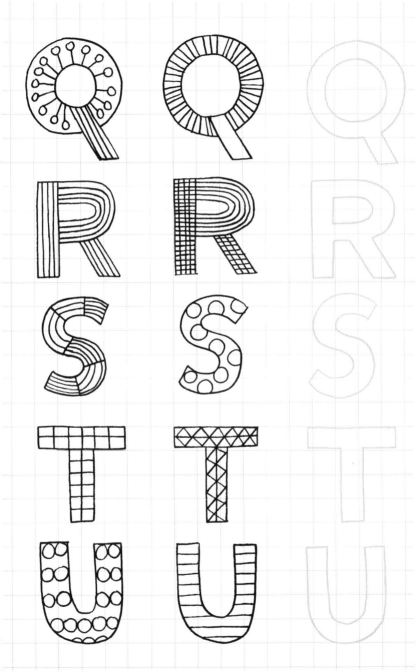

Decorate the leaves and colour in.

Complete and add texture.

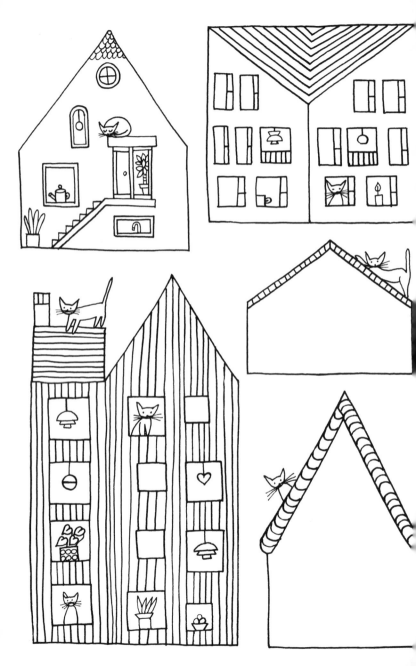

Add windows and doors.

Decorate
the vine
leaves.

EVERYTHING
BEGINS WITH
A DOT

Wassily Kandinsky

Connect the dots to create a pattern.

Decorate with zigzags, spots, stripes and checks.

Create your own butterflies.

Complete
the geese.

Complete the page.

Adorn the pots
with patterns.

Add patterns to the leaves.

Add windows and doors.

Complete the mice.

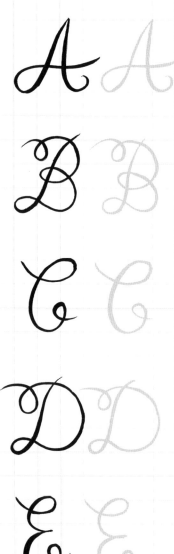

Here's a curly calligraphy exercise for you.

Meditate

Quiet

Now

Tranquil

Relax

Practise your calligraphy by tracing these mindful words.

Add detail to the bear.

Tessellate.

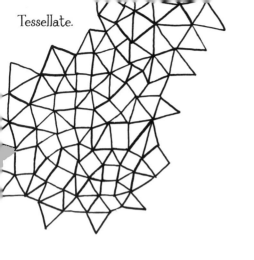

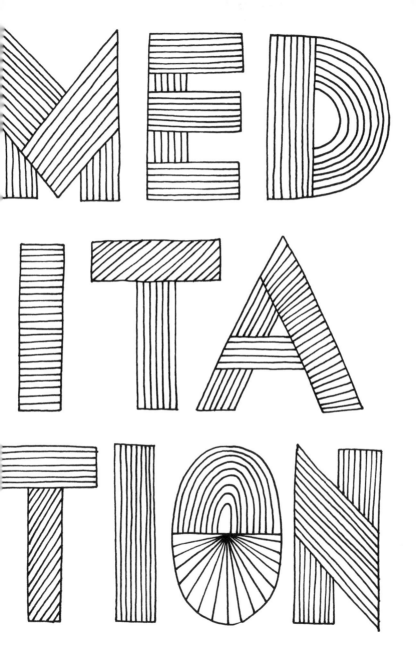

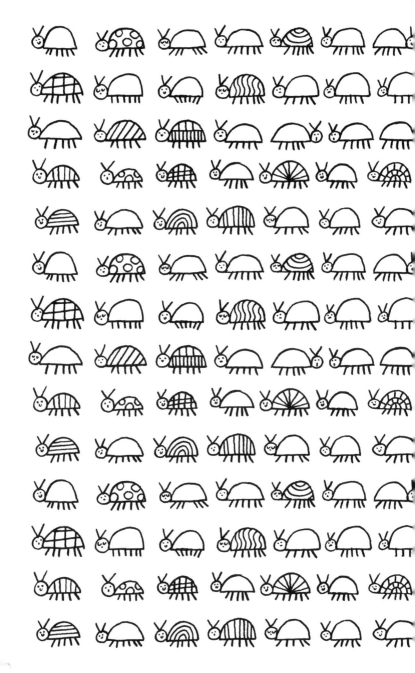

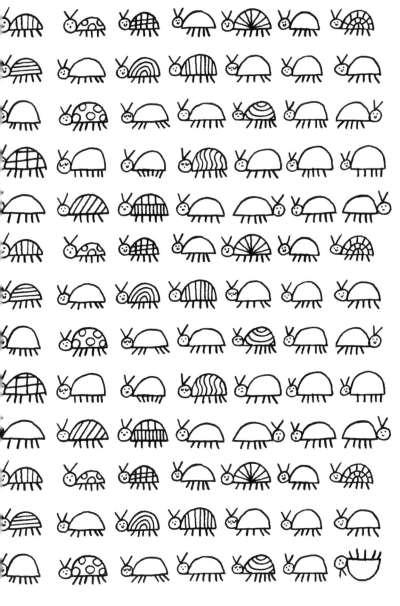

Some of these ladybirds need to be decorated.

Complete the butterfly.

THANKS

To my two year old Viggo, for reminding me
daily about the goodness of being present.

EMMA FARRARONS
illustration & art direction

www.emmafarrarons.com

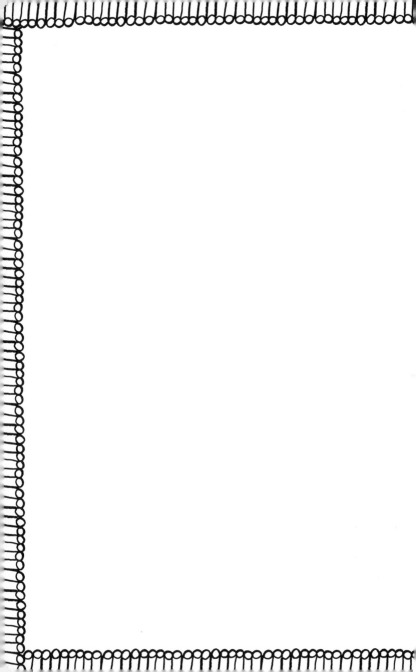